GRADE **02**

PIANO

Pieces & Exercises for
Trinity College London
Exams 2018–2020

Includes CD &
teaching notes

Published by
Trinity College London Press
trinitycollege.com

Registered in England
Company no. 09726123

Printed in England by Halstan & Co Ltd., Amersham, Bucks

The Marionettes

(duet part)

Stanisław Prószyński
(1926-1997)

The Marionettes

(candidate's part)

Stanisław Prószyński
(1926-1997)

Almost a Canon

Arr. Haas

Johann Joseph Fux
(1660-1741)

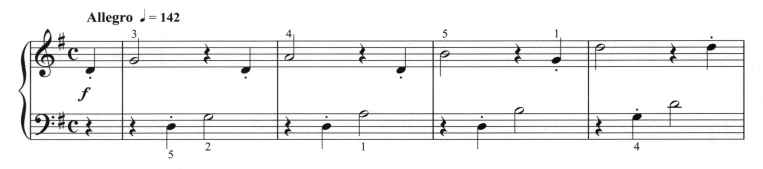

Rigaudon

Georg Philipp Telemann
(1681-1767)

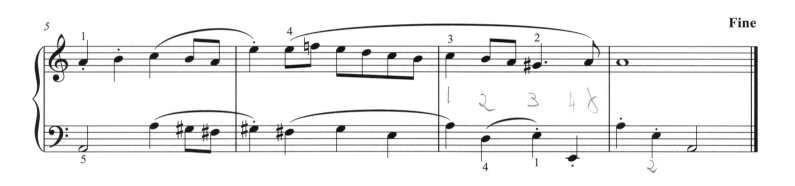

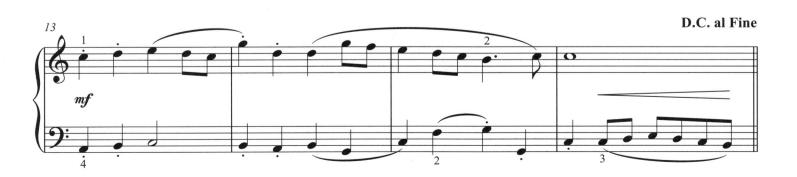

5

Balletto

Arr. Haas

Georg Simon Löhlein
(1725–1781)

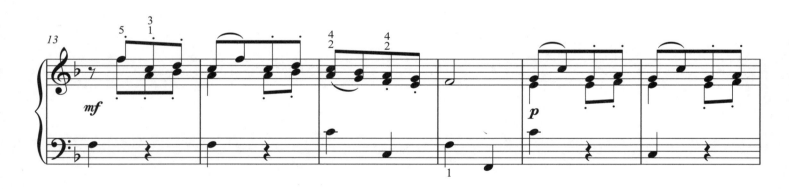

The Rowboat

Felicitas Kukuck
(1914-2001)

The Ballerina

Ray Moore
(b. 1939)

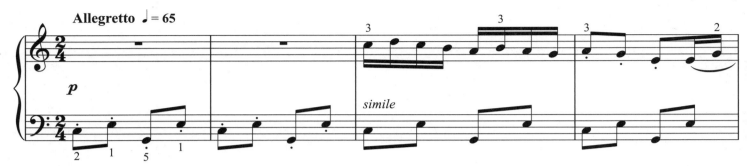

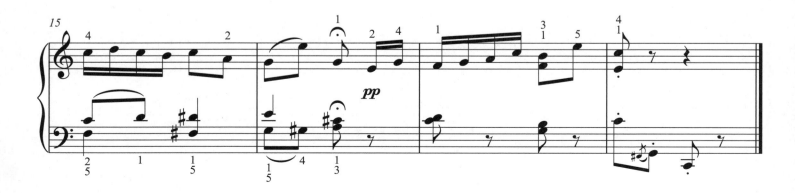

Shepherd's Melody

Rainer Mohrs
(b. 1953)

Do not play the repeat in the exam.

Persian Holiday

Sam Cleaver
(b. 1982)

Poor Mouse

Vera Mohrs
(b. 1984)

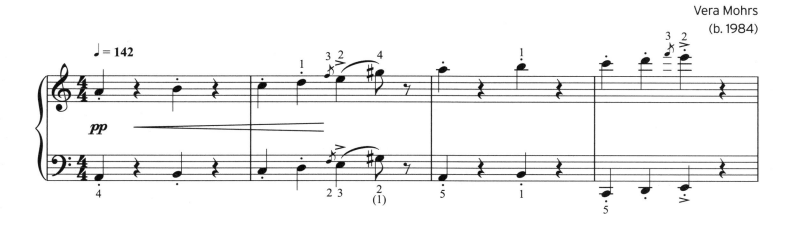

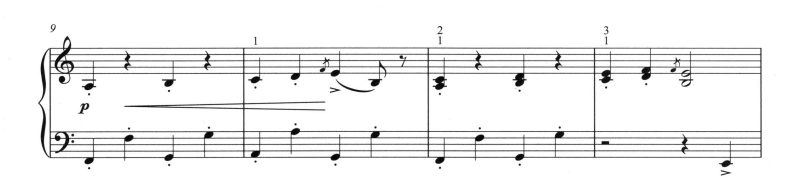

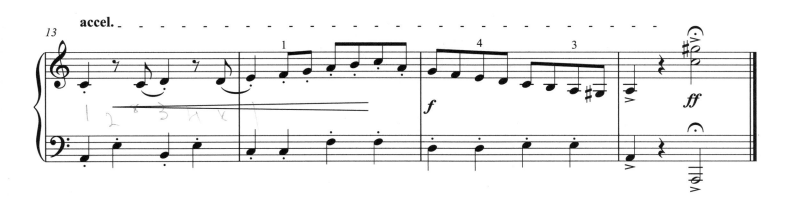

11

Exercises

1a. Handing Over – tone, balance and voicing

1b. A Baroque Formation – tone, balance and voicing

12

2a. Off-centre – co-ordination

2b. Quick March – co-ordination

3a. Late Night Lullaby – finger & wrist strength and flexibility

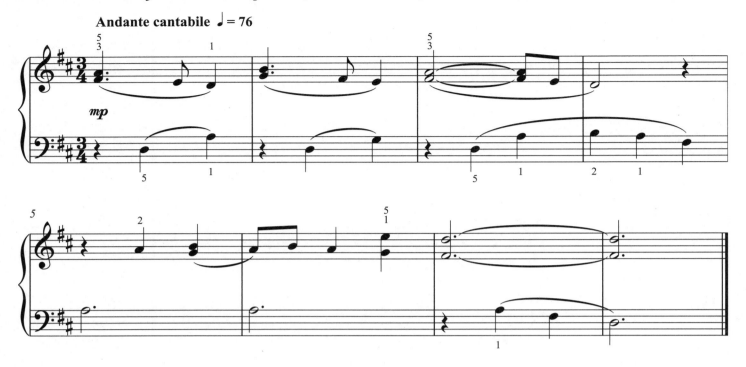

3b. Rockhopper – finger & wrist strength and flexibility

Teaching notes

Prószyński   The Marionettes (duet)   page 2

This is enormous fun and at the recommended brisk tempo should be a good party piece as well. There is a long tradition of puppetry in Eastern Europe – think of Martinů's *Loutky* or that the story of *Faust* toured Europe as a puppet play before Christopher Marlowe put it on the London stage. Prószyński has in mind here the mechanical, stiff-jointed movements of the marionettes, reproduced through absolute rhythmic precision, a sharp *staccato* and sudden, dramatic dynamic changes. Perhaps too there is an element of *Punch and Judy* here, with the violent *forte* accents and the *accelerando* as they chase each other off stage at the end?

To get that precise, crisp *staccato* keep the movements small and energised, staying close to the keys. Fingering is as important in *staccato* as in *legato*, but it is easier to change position in the former, so consider whether beginning the RH on 5 is the most reliable option. Sometimes we want to give a fraction of time for *subito* dynamic changes, but that wouldn't be appropriate here. Nevertheless you need to think ahead, preparing in your mind for your fingers to find a different touch, a slower or faster speed of depression. The chords in bars 19 & 23 could be longer, matching the RH. Try ending on 5, perhaps 1, 2, 3, 5, or even using both hands, to give a final kick on the last note.

Fux *arr.* Haas   Almost a Canon   page 4

Johann Joseph Fux was born in 1660 and is probably most well known for setting down in print the rules of counterpoint, rules that are still followed today when students write in strict counterpoint. This small teaching piece has been edited, but the added articulation and dynamic detail is eminently sensible and results in a *scherzando* mood with sudden dynamic changes, crossing parts and a sense of mocking the seriousness of genuine counterpoint.

Listen for the difference between a crotchet that is purposefully *staccato* and a crotchet that gently releases at the end of a slur. They should feel and sound different. The unison D on the last beat of bars 5, 7 and 16 needs a decision: play with RH, LH or both? You want to hear both parts but, especially as both hands would be using thumbs, there is a danger that it could be too loud if played by both. An excellent Kodály exercise to use is to sing one hand while playing the other, developing the ability to genuinely hear two lines at once. I would suggest keeping the bass line *legato* in bars 12–14, and watch out for some sneakily tricky co-ordination at the very end. Finally, this is light-hearted; have in mind a fun occasion and replicate that mood for your audience.

Telemann   Rigaudon   page 5

The Rigaudon is an old French dance, probably from Provençal, and this one captures some of this dance's peasant roots, with its obstinate rhythmic repetitions and straightforward structure. There would probably have been very little musical detail in the original, but the editorial decisions here are good, allowing the hands mostly to synchronise articulation, but with a few exceptions. Perfect for developing independence of the hands and also the ability to listen to two separate lines. Multi-tasking is no problem for pianists...

Telemann was a contemporary of J S Bach and although we may think of the baroque style as being very serious today, the word was originally used to mean something over-decorative or fanciful. Baroque music was often embellished, particularly secular works – just think of all those Handel *da capo* arias that kept the audience enthralled as sopranos and castrati vied with each other to add ever more virtuosic ornamentation. This Rigaudon is not really a piece of that ilk, but you may like to add a three-note mordent on the G♯ in bar 7 in the *da capo*.

Löhlein *arr.* Haas   Balletto   page 6

The main technical challenge here is the thirds, played *staccato* and *legato* in the RH. If thirds are relatively new to you, then this is a good opportunity to tackle them – the demands here are very reasonable and appropriate at this level – but try doing some work on them before learning this piece. Play C major in *staccato* thirds or in slurred pairs, then F major with its B♭ an added hurdle. Listen for perfect synchronisation of the two notes, achieved through having the fingers already on the keys, then using the arm to ensure both play together, keeping the wrist stable, but flexible. There are two fingerings suggested for the same pattern here, in bars 1 and 9. I instinctively began with 2, 1 for the first third, but then moved to 3, 1 for the third quaver, returning to 2, 1 at the beginning of the next bar. So now you have three alternatives to try!

Georg Simon Löhlein was an early classical composer, working in Leipzig for much of his life as a performer and teacher. He wrote important teaching books for both piano and violin, so it is not surprising that this thirds exercise is so well-constructed. The whole piece uses just the two chords of tonic and dominant 7th. Quite ingenious, making the notes easy to learn and throwing all attention on to mastering the thirds and communicating the piece's character. By giving it the title 'Balletto' and having *mf* as the loudest dynamic, Löhlein is asking for elegance, control, gracefulness in execution; the tempo is quite challenging and should be seen as a maximum. Listen for the crotchet rests in the cellos, for the shaping of the two-note slurs, for the different characterisation of the *piano* phrases. A useful exercise in the guise of a piece!

Kukuck   The Rowboat   page 7

This is a rather lazy, almost soulful, trip on a rowboat. It is not essential, but if pianists can reach the pedal then this could be a good piece for pedalling practice, with a change every two beats giving plenty of time to master the technique. Learn to do it quite rhythmically: down before you start, then up/down on the first two quavers of the bar, up/down on quavers 4 & 5 etc. Practise on a scale played with one finger, listening to the notes being linked by the pedal, and have a look at what is happening inside the piano if possible so that you understand how the dampers work. There are places where the pedal is not needed, for instance the last two bars, but generally the effect is good.

Using the pedal will help the sense of gliding on the stream, but it is by no means necessary to play the piece well and would be inappropriate for those who cannot reach the pedals. Instead, hold on to the minim chords for as long as possible before you have to release to repeat the bass note. The melodic line moves into the LH in bar 3, so keep the RH quavers lighter here. We say that sometimes when Schubert moves into the major the effect is to deepen the sadness, invoking bitter-sweet memories of a happiness that will not return. There's something of this in the final bars as our trip comes to an end and we return to dry soil.

Moore   The Ballerina   page 8

The ballerina depicted here sounds rather young and inexperienced, eliciting an 'aah' from all who watch. She loses balance for a moment in bar 10, gains confidence for her biggest leap yet in bar 16, then shyly runs off stage at the end. The challenge will be to keep the delicacy and sweetness in this; the tempo is moderate and the bass sets the mood with gentle *pizzicato* quavers. As always, fingers stay close to, if not on, the keys, and see the picture, imagine the sound you want before you begin.

The RH semiquavers want to be beautifully even and smooth, a graceful arm movement before the gentle foot taps on the quavers. Small wrist movements will help the slurs in bars 4 & 5, and the whole arm should be involved in the accent in bar 10. Keep the pattern of smooth semiquavers, short quavers in bar 15, and imagine this picture of increasing self-belief for the *f* here, finding a sound that is confident, rather than strident. You may like to do some re-arranging in the tricky last *pp* bars, perhaps taking the RH F and E into the LH to make the melody easier to control, or the last middle C into the RH to give the LH more time to prepare the *acciaccatura*. Understated, subtle and rather lovely.

R Mohrs	Shepherd's Melody	page 9

Both hands remain in a G position throughout, but this clever piece contrasts a rather doleful *Largo* section with a dancing central *Allegro*. Minor becomes major; bare open fifths turn into harmonic major thirds; the tempo more than doubles. Find a story behind the transformation: something happens to change the lonely shepherd's mood – a passing circus? watching a family of rabbits chase each other through the field? Whatever it is disappears, and he returns to his melancholy...

This is another piece where some discreet pedalling would help to link the drone chords, just as the breath through bagpipes also helps to make the sound continuous. But the piece works perfectly well without. Remember to make the *forte/piano* contrast in both hands in bars 11-13, relating the dynamic levels to the mood, not allowing the *forte* to shout. You may like to move the LH to play the thirds in the middle section with 2 & 4, a better balanced hand perhaps, changing back to a G position for bar 23. Allegro is a tempo marking but also implies liveliness, and here there should be no pedal, and the unslurred quavers will sound more light-hearted if articulated. No repeat, but the *da capo* is essential.

Cleaver	Persian Holiday	page 10

The bass motif makes me think of camels, their humps swinging from side to side, and the augmented 2nds in the melody are of course shorthand for the East. Both these elements are immediately appealing but don't be fooled, this is a tricky little piece, full of articulation detail that demands complete independence of the hands. An excellent workout for the brain.

Find a comfortable swing within the hand to achieve the bass slurs. This is something of a caricature, so you can enjoy the drop-float effect, always ensuring that the fifth finger does not play on its side. We often forget that the thumb also moves independently – playing it with the whole hand will make it heavy, and here you need to avoid that. Once the physical movements of the LH are engrained, it will be easier to maintain the integrity of the melody's articulation on top of the camel's lurching gait. Begin bar 15 softer than the dynamic you've reached to make the *crescendo* effective and keep the *ff* in the context of an energetic holiday excursion – fun, not fierce!

V Mohrs	Poor Mouse	page 11

The story here is crystal clear, the only question is whether the chord at the end is the cat getting the mouse, or the mouse finally escaping... perhaps the title provides the answer!

The *acciaccaturas*, crushed notes, help emphasise the accents. We would expect the one in bar 2 to be D♯ to E, so approaching the E from above is an inventive surprise. Experiment with fingering – I found 3, 2 in RH and 3, 4 in LH easier to synchronise. There are two places, bar 12, LH, and bar 16, both hands, where we have crotchets that are neither *staccato* nor slurred, so hold these for their full length. Each line has a *crescendo* (the mouse trying to leave its hole?), dropping back again at the beginning of the following line, with the final *crescendo* taking you all the way to the *ff* climax. It's not easy to start *pp* on a piano you don't know, but you need to take a risk, barely pressing to the bottom of the key. Have that pulse ticking away in your head before you start – perhaps sing the first line through to yourself to find the tempo and character. Keep to the suggested brisk speed; the mouse is justifiably jittery, the cat poised to pounce. Just one note of caution: the aim is to excite your audience, not necessarily to get excited yourself. A warm heart and cool head will help you communicate the mood, but stay technically in control.

Crosland	Bendin' the Rules	*Ferrum*

This is a rather simple piece at this level, so examiners will be looking for all the musical details to be fully incorporated into the performance. Two in a bar with a variety of articulations: a sharp, cheeky *staccato*, edgy accents, weighted and slinky slurs. Some of the last are two-note slurs with lightly released second crotchets, but some end on a *staccato*, implying a more active, strongly played last note. Bars 13- 15 have the same music as the opening, but suggest a different arrangement of the hands. It may be worth experimenting with using this at the beginning, as long as the RH knows exactly where to find its chord in bar 3.

Once all the detail is in place, the mood should look after itself. Jaunty, swaggering, confident. Note though that there is nothing aggressive about the piece; the main dynamic is *mf*, which gives room for the accents to make their mark without having to shout. An extra thrust from the arms should help with the *sfz* at the end. At ♩ = 76 the whole piece should take precisely one minute. Perfect!

Gurlitt	Peasant Dance (duet)	Breitkopf

This duet gives the RH a good workout. Firm, well-supported fingers staying close to the keys and played with plenty of energy from the bridge of the hand will find the *f* at speed that is requested. Avoid making the arm heavy; remember that the note needs to be depressed *quickly* to sound *forte*, and you want to feel the release in each finger as soon as it has played. No pressing down with the arm or hand. The frequent *staccatos* are useful, places where you can check that the wrist is completely free. Listen for rhythmic evenness in the semiquavers and adjust the fingering if you need to. It's good to practise bar 4 using fingers 5 & 4, but in performance you may find 3 & 2 more dependable. At the *p* imagine that one of the dancers has a solo, then all the others join in again as the opening music returns in bar 13. ♩ = 92, and observe the *scherzando* – this needs to sound as though the performer is having fun, so get an appropriate picture in your head before you start.

Haydn	German Dance	*Kjos*

Haydn was undoubtedly one of the great classical composers, in many ways making possible the often more lauded developments of Beethoven. But they all had to start somewhere and they used to practise writing small pieces to harmonic formulas; I suspect this is one such. An opening fanfare delineates the bright D major triad, a more elegant reply deploys a small sequence, then cadences in D. The following four bars unceremoniously take us to A major, the elegant theme returns and all is over in under a minute at ♩ = 126. No repeats in the exam.

Formulaic to some extent, but are there traces of Haydn's future eminence? I enjoy the contrast between the stronger sections that have three equal beats in a bar and what I've labelled above as the elegant reply, which favours the first beat, eschewing any chord on beat three, and sounding momentarily more like a graceful Minuet. As well as listening for the difference in stress between these sections, you may like to add a little dynamic variation to highlight the characters of each line. There is something satisfying about it – perfectly balanced and with a nod to a more French elegance that softens its opening directness.

Knipper	A Cavalry Song of the Steppes	*Breitkopf*

Lev Knipper studied with Reinhold Glière, another composer often favoured by examination boards, and fought in the Russian civil war. This cavalry song is melancholy, bleak and heavy-hearted, but also rather haunting with its use of the flattened seventh and primary triads in root position. The Russian steppes are vast grasslands and the weariness entailed in crossing them is manifest in these dark, stern bass chords. A crotchet beat of 104 captures the determined, but weary mood.

It is worth trying different fingerings on the triad. 1, 3, 5 may suit many, but 1, 2, 4 is also an option. I like to use the latter on the C minor chord, then the former as the hand goes down to G minor in bar 4 – it makes the two chords seem more connected. Perfect synchronisation of all three notes may take some practice. Try just playing the open fifth first, making sure the hand is well-balanced, then add in the third, usually a black note, making sure to have all three fingers resting on the notes before you play them. It's also important that the chords allow the melodic material to be in the spotlight. Keep them separated, but all the same length, no pedal, and no more than *mf* (probably *mp* from bar 11). Use plenty of arm weight to make a full, vibrant sound for the melody, keeping it *legato* above the chords. Have a picture in your mind before you start − see those soldiers in their ushankas on horseback looking out over the steppes...

Lvov-Kompaneets The Sparrow   *Trinity*

This descriptive piece in C major relies on a lightness of touch and spirit for its effect. Pay careful attention to the articulation markings, making sure to phrase off the slurred groups delicately, and to give emphasis to the *tenuto* crotchets (bar 4, 20, etc).

The piece is in ternary (ABA) form, the B section (bars 9-16) in the dominant key of G major and marked *forte*. The composer has an interesting surprise for us when the A section returns. Several unexpected flats appear in the last phrase, outlining the chord of Db major (in the key of C major this chord is known as the Neapolitan 6th). What effect does this have on the mood, for you?

Lysenko   Raindrops   *Breitkopf*

These raindrops have not kept you inside, rather you seem to be out there among them, running around and thoroughly enjoying the experience. Even the forays into A minor remain cheerful and the final *sf* is positively triumphant. A crotchet pulse of 76 is good.

Melodic movement is mostly by step and fits extremely well under the hands. The *staccato* wants to be very light and crisp to recreate the rain, but that doesn't mean lifting high off the keys. Staying close to the keys is always safer, more economical, and usually makes a more precise sound. Keep the wrist supple to help shape the small slurs and use the arms to give extra thrust for the last chord. You can make up exercises away from the keyboard to help the hands achieve independence of articulation; games like playing a scale *legato* in one hand while singing *staccato*, and vice versa, are also fun to try. I would also get pianists to imagine a story behind the music. Why C major in places and A minor in others? Why *p* here and *mf* there? What happens at the end? This will help cement the dynamics in their minds and bring the whole piece to life.

A Whole New World
Menken   (from Walt Disney's *Aladdin*)   *Faber*

'I can show you the world / Shining, shimmering splendid / Tell me, princess, now when did / You last let your heart decide!' sings Aladdin as he and the princess fly on his magic carpet. You can watch the clip from the film on YouTube; Aladdin is rather free with his rhythms and the tempo is quite fast. For the purposes of the exam, ♩ = 96 moves without hurrying, allowing plenty of time to find the chords; just the second repeat; and the rhythms should be played as notated!

Pedal is indicated just at the end, but be sure to check the pedals before you start. Some pianos have three, and all of us have pressed the wrong one by mistake at some point! The chord playing here is quite sophisticated, and it is never too early to get ingrained some good practice. For instance, substituting fingers: the suggested fingering in RH bar 18 is not ideal, completely breaking the melodic connection between the C and G. My preferred option would be to substitute a 2 for the thumb on the F on beat 2, then play the third chord with 3/1. Not essential, but a useful technique. Knowing and loving the tune will make many want to choose this, but it isn't an easy option by any means...

Strecke   Rustic Dance   *Breitkopf*

There are several imaginative pieces by Kerstin Strecke in the syllabus. She was trained both as a pianist and artist and now works as both in Frankfurt.

The harmonies here are simply tonic and dominant, justifying the 'rustic' tag. But the key is A major, so a little further away from C than usual, and a good key to explore, with longer fingers fitting neatly on to the black notes in chords and scales. I would suggest learning the tune without the chords, swapping between hands as necessary − it's so good to have the LH share the spotlight. Then see if you can work out which chord fits under each bar just by listening: is that a comfortable tonic bar, or is it a bar with more tension, needing the dominant 7th under it? Hear the two chords as tension and resolution, shaping the phrases accordingly − this is the basis for so much music and beyond. No repeats in the exam please, and a tempo around ♩ = 120.

Terzibaschitsch   The Little Locomotive   *Trinity*

What a clever idea this is, to have the train accelerate out of one station, chug away to the next, and then gradually apply the brakes. Probably not the first time it's been done, but effective nonetheless. The main body of the piece can go at a locomotive speed, around 192 chugs (crotchets) per minute. This is another piece that uses just two chords, tonic and dominant 7th, so spend some time feeling confident about them, playing them in all inversions, as arpeggios, broken chords, etc. Then you are off: just two positions in the LH to find and, as I suggested elsewhere (see Strecke above), see if pianists can hear which chord it should be under the RH melody, rather than just read it. They should learn to identify the bars that move away from home, from the tonic, and improvising on these chords may also be useful to develop this aural skill.

Be sure to get both hands involved in the whistle blasts − maybe the ensuing *p* is because someone has covered their ears? The *accelerando* at the beginning always seems much easier than the *ritardando* at the end. To help the latter, keep hearing the LH crotchets in your head through those rests, getting slower and slower...and stop.

Terzibaschitsch   The Gondola (duet)   *Trinity*

Based almost entirely on two gently rocking harmonies, this is quite a hypnotic duet, and the secondo is repetitive enough to perhaps enable a friend to be involved, preferably one who can add in the pedal as well. Marked 'sad', this is not the usual serenade on a gondola, but perhaps a trip made alone, remembering a time when you were with friends. Hear the LH taking over the melody in bar 7 and passing it back to the RH in bar 8. Both hands will play the same phrase in unison a few bars later and this is a tricky moment for the LH, involving either a big stretch (you could start on 5 and stretch to the thumb for the higher E) or crossing over up a fifth. If you choose the latter, as is indicated in the score, then remember that the pedal is managing the *legato* for you and it is legal to let go in order to make the movement smooth and avoid raising the elbow. The addition of the *pp* notes in bars 23 & 25 is a nice touch from Terzibaschitsch, and will require a sensitive touch from pianists, light fingers, barely pressing to the bottom of the keys. Synchronise the last chord by breathing together. Keen-eyed pianists will spot the missing tie in the LH in bar 18.

The drawing of a rather nervous dinosaur at the bottom of the page is most definitely not a pterodactyl but this popular book starring prehistoric animals is useful to have for pianists going through the obligatory dinosaur phase. A jazz waltz is one that leaves out the third beat in the accompaniment – think Satie's *Gymnopédies* – giving a more relaxed mood to the whole.

There are some ambiguities in the marked articulation. Does the slur in bars 3-4 imply non-*legato* in bars 1 & 2? My suggestion would be to see the slurs as riding on the thermals, swooping and ultra *legato*, whereas elsewhere perhaps you're needing to flap those enormous wings to stay up there, so find more buoyancy in the *legato*. Meanwhile that descending semitone bass line in the rather beautiful B minor middle section – ah, it works every time doesn't it? – suggests to me that you could detach the bass notes in the first section, throwing a little more emphasis on to the chord, whose top note shadows the melody. Schubert often uses accents where he wants an emotional stress, and I think that is the case in bar 18. You don't want to hit the top A, but realise its expressiveness against the bass A♯ and colour accordingly. Wedgwood's tempo and words of advice are excellent as always.

Teaching notes written by Pamela Lidiard

Key

A solid line denotes a piece within this book.

A dotted line denotes a piece from the alternative list.